www.colorfulcreativekids.com

Visit our website for ***freebies***!

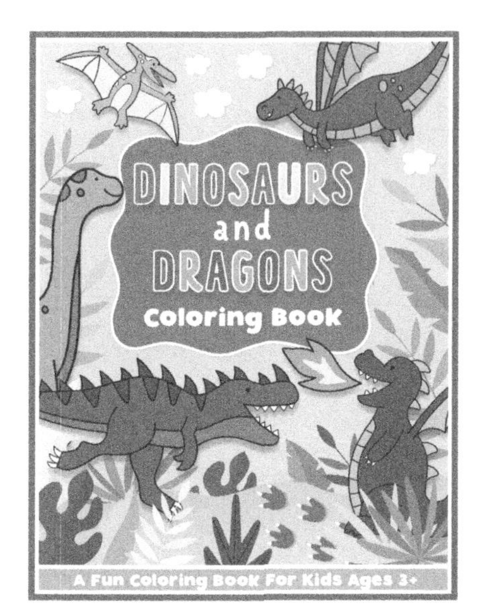

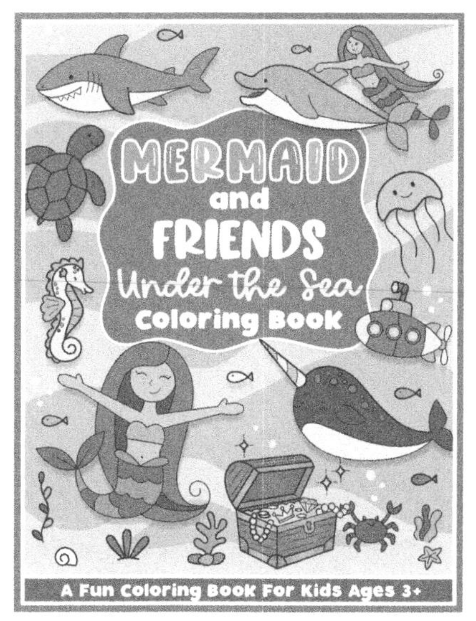

On our website you'll find all of our coloring and activity books, downloadable pages, merchandise, coloring videos, and more!

We value your feedback! Please leave us a book review online or contact us through our website.

Hello! My name is Amber, the illustrator, and owner of Colorful Creative Kids; thank you so much for purchasing this coloring book! As a mom, I understand that taking the time to research quality and authentic products that entertain, educate, and induce creativity in our little ones is very important. This is why each coloring and activity page was hand-sketched and converted to a digital image, generating clean and consistent lines to create an enjoyable experience for younger artists! I hope it brings your child hours of coloring and activity fun and ignites their creative spark!

Colorful Creative Kids is a Veteran and Woman Owned Small Business and sincerely appreciates your purchase and feedback. Please take a few moments to leave a review online!

For more information about CCK, visit us at www.colorfulcreativekids.com or contact us at info@colorfulcreativekids.com.

Copyright Notice

Illustrated & Produced by Colorful Creative Kids

Mermaid and Friends Under the Sea Coloring and Workbook

Colorful Creative Kids is a DBA for DOOTLS, LLC

ISBN: ***978-1-7361660-2-4***

Hello! My name is Amber, the illustrator and owner of Colorful Creative Kids [illegible]
[illegible]
creative [illegible]

[illegible]

For more information [illegible] visit [illegible] colorfulcreativekids.com or contact [illegible]
[illegible]

Copyright Notice

Created & Published by Colorful Creative Kids

Mermaid and Friends [illegible]

[illegible] Copyright [illegible] LLC

Colorful Creative Kids [illegible] LLC.

[illegible] LLC

ISBN: 978-1-7361660-2-4